Disney

THE JUNGLE BOOK

Mowgli Meets Baloo

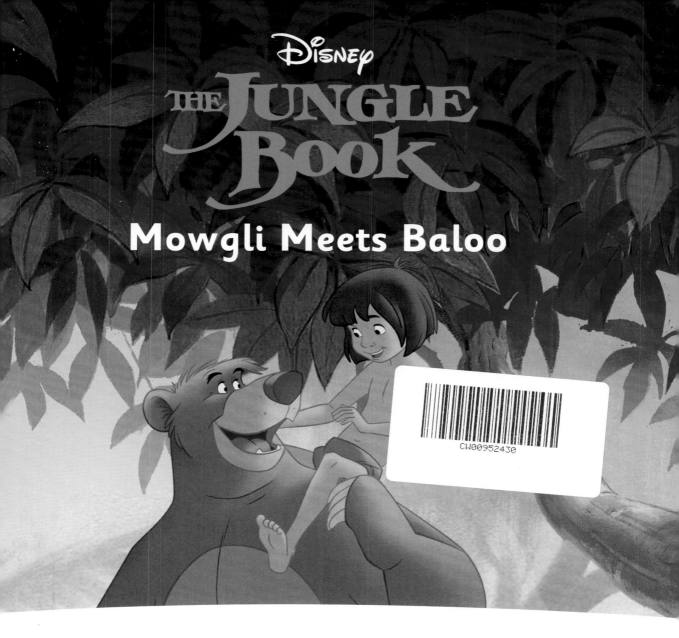

Level 2

Re-told by: Nicola Schofield
Series Editor: Rachel Wilson

Before You Read

In This Book

Mowgli

Shere Khan

Baloo

Activity

Read and say.

1 Mowgli and Baloo are ...
  a friends
  b pets
  c brothers

2 Shere Khan is ...
  a friendly
  b nice
  c dangerous

3 They live in the ...
  a ocean
  b jungle
  c town

Mowgli is a young boy. He's ten. He lives
in the jungle with the animals.
The jungle is hot.

Some animals are his friends.
The panther, the elephant, and the monkey
play with Mowgli. They like him.

But not all the animals like him.
The snake wants to eat Mowgli!

Shere Khan is a dangerous tiger.
He doesn't like Mowgli. He wants Mowgli
to leave the jungle.

Mowgli is a boy and boys don't live
in the jungle.
Shere Khan follows him.

Mowgli is angry and scared. Shere Khan
is dangerous, but what can Mowgli do?
Who can help him now?

Suddenly, Mowgli meets a friendly bear.
The bear's name is Baloo. Baloo is nice!
Mowgli tells him about Shere Khan.

Mowgli is sad. The jungle is his home.
He doesn't want to leave.

Baloo wants to help this young boy.
He doesn't want Mowgli to be sad.

Baloo carries Mowgli and smiles at him.
Mowgli laughs. He isn't scared of the
tiger now.

Baloo and Mowgli walk together in the jungle. They're friends now.

The two friends play in the jungle.
They swim in the river. Then they eat
bananas! They have fun together.

Baloo likes to dance. He's a funny bear!

Baloo and Mowgli are tired, but Mowgli is happy again. "Thank you, Baloo!" he says. They're great friends.

After You Read

1 **Point and say.**

   1 bear
   2 elephant
   3 panther
   4 snake
   5 tiger

2 **Who does this? Match the sentences to the characters.**

> Mowgli   Shere Khan   Baloo

   1 He follows Mowgli.
   2 He carries Mowgli.
   3 He plays with the animals.

3 **Read and say Yes or No.**

   1 Mowgli lives with his family.
   2 Shere Khan is a friendly tiger.
   3 Mowgli and Baloo are friends.
   4 Mowgli likes the jungle.

Picture Dictionary

dangerous

elephant

friendly

have fun

jungle

monkey

panther

river

snake

together

Phonics

Say the sounds. Read the words.

A a

cat

sad

O o

dog

hot

U u

fun

run

Say the rhyme.

The jungle is hot. The river is not.
A panther is a cat. It doesn't have a hat.
It runs and jumps. It does not stop.

Values

Help your friends.

What do you know about the rainforest?

In the rainforest, it's hot and sunny ... and it rains!
Some trees in the rainforest grow very tall. Some trees are very old.
Coconuts, bananas and mangoes all grow here.
Interesting and important plants and animals live in the rainforest.
The rainforest helps all life on Earth.

plant

mango

coconut

a monkey in a tree

Pearson Education Limited
KAO Two
KAO Park, Harlow,
Essex, CMI7 9NA, England
and Associated Companies throughout the world.

ISBN: 978-1-2923-4668-7

This edition first published by Pearson Education Ltd 2020

1 3 5 7 9 10 8 6 4 2

Set in Heinemann Roman Special, 19pt/28pt
Printed by Neografia, Slovakia

Published by Pearson Education Limited

Acknowledgments
Getty Images: apomares/ E+ 21, Daugirdas Tomas Racys/ Moment 18, Mayur Kakade/ Moment 18, Suttipong Sutiratanachai/ Moment 20-21
Shutterstock.com: Olena Brodetska 18, Pesek Photo 21, puwanai 17, Quick Shot.16

For a complete list of the titles available in the Pearson English Readers series, visit www.pearsonenglishreaders.com.

Alternatively, write to your local Pearson Education office or to Pearson English Readers Marketing Department, Pearson Education, KAO Two, KAO Park, Harlow, Essex, CMI7 9NA